How to be Brilliant at

ELECTRICITY, LIGHT & SOUND

Colin Hughes
Winnie Wade

We hope you and your class enjoy using this book. Other books in the series include:

Science titles

How to be Brilliant at Recording in Science	1 897675 10 0
How to be Brilliant at Science Investigations	1 897675 11 9
How to be Brilliant at Materials	1 897675 12 7

English titles

How to be Brilliant at Writing Stories	1 897675 00 3
How to be Brilliant at Writing Poetry	1 897675 01 1
How to be Brilliant at Grammar	1 897675 02 X
How to be Brilliant at Making Books	1 897675 03 8
How to be Brilliant at Spelling	1 897675 08 9
How to be Brilliant at Reading	1 897675 09 7

Maths titles

How to be Brilliant at Using a Calculator	1 897675 04 6
How to be Brilliant at Algebra	1 897675 05 4
How to be Brilliant at Numbers	1 897675 06 2
How to be Brilliant at Shape and Space	1 897675 07 0
How to be Brilliant at Mental Arithmetic	1 897675 21 6

History and Geography titles

How to be Brilliant at Recording in History	1 897675 22 4
How to be Brilliant at Recording in Geography	1 897675 31 3

If you would like further information on these or other titles published by Brilliant Publications, please write to the address given below.

Published by Brilliant Publications,
The Old School Yard, Leighton Road, Northall,
Dunstable, Bedfordshire LU6 2HA

Written by Colin Hughes and Winnie Wade
Illustrated by Kate Ford
Cover photograph by Martyn Chillmaid

Printed in Malta by Interprint Ltd

© Colin Hughes and Winnie Wade 1997
ISBN 1 897675 13 5

First published in 1997
Reprinted 1999
10 9 8 7 6 5 4 3 2

Contents

Introduction

How to be Brilliant at Electricity, Light and Sound contains over 40 photocopiable sheets for use with children working at levels 2-5 of the National Curriculum (Scottish levels C-E). The activities are designed to help children develop the scientific knowledge and understanding of these topics. They can be used whenever the need arises for particular activities to support and supplement your existing scheme of work for science. The activities provide learning experiences which can be tailored to meet individual children's needs.

The activities are addressed directly to the children. They are self-contained and many children will be able to work with little additional support from you. You may have some pupils, however, who have the necessary scientific skills and concepts, but require your help in reading the sheets.

Pupils should be encouraged to use the sheets for all aspects of communicating their work. Most of the activities require basic classroom science resources and these are listed in the **What you need** box on each sheet. Some of the sheets require the use of an additional resource sheet. Where this is the case, it has been indicated by a small box, with the page number in it, in the top right corner, eg 48 .

Links to the National Curriculum
How to be Brilliant at Electricity, Light and Sound relates directly to themes 1 and 3 of the programmes of study for Physical Processes. Pages 5 and 6 give details of those elements of the programme of study that are covered.

Links to the National Curriculum

How to be Brilliant at Electricity, Light and Sound supports the following elements of the Physical Processes programme of study.

Pupils should be taught:

1 Electricity

simple circuits

a   that a complete circuit, including a battery or power supply, is needed to make electrical devices work;

b   how switches can be used to control electrical devices;

c   ways of varying the current in a circuit to make bulbs brighter or dimmer;

d   how to represent series circuits by drawings and diagrams, and how to construct series circuits on the basis of drawings and diagrams.

3 Light and sound

everyday effects of light

a   that light travels from a source;

b   that light cannot pass through some materials, and that this leads to the formation of shadows;

c   that light is reflected from surfaces, *eg mirrors, polished metals*;

seeing

d   that we see light sources, *eg light bulbs, candles*, because light from them enters our eyes;

vibration and sound

e   that sounds are made when objects, *eg strings on musical instruments*, vibrate but that vibrations are not always directly visible;

f   that the pitch and loudness of sounds produced by some vibrating objects, *eg a drum skin, a plucked string*, can be changed;

g   that vibrations from sound sources can travel through a variety of materials, *eg metals, wood, glass, air*, to the ear.

In addition, the requirements in the following section of the programme of study (National Curriculum, 1995) apply across the Physical Processes.

Pupils should be given opportunities to:

1 Systematic enquiry

a   ask questions related to their work in science;

b   use focused exploration and investigation to acquire scientific knowledge, understanding and skills;

c   use both first-hand experience and secondary sources to obtain information;

d   use IT to collect, store, retrieve and present scientific information.

2   Science in everyday life

a   use their knowledge and understanding of science to explain and interpret a range of familiar phenomena;

b   consider the part science has played in the development of many of the things that they use;

c   relate their understanding of science to their personal health;

d   consider ways in which living things and the environment need protection.

3   The nature of scientific ideas

a   obtain evidence to test scientific ideas in a variety of ways;

b   recognize that science provides explanations for many phenomena.

Pupils should be taught to:

4   Communication

a   use appropriate scientific vocabulary to describe and explain the behaviour of living things, materials and processes;

b   use standard measures and SI units, *eg metre, newton*, appropriate to their work;

c   use a wide range of methods, including diagrams, drawings, graphs, tables and charts, to record and present information in an appropriate and systematic manner.

5   Health and safety

a   recognize and assess the hazards and risks to themselves and others when working with living things and materials;

b   take action to control these risks.

What uses electricity?

Did you know that one hundred years ago very few houses had electricity?

So many things in our lives today depend on electricity. From the moment we get up, to the time we go to sleep, we are surrounded by machines, toys and appliances which use electricity.

Look carefully at the picture below. Which appliances are using electricity? Is the electricity provided by the mains supply or by batteries? Record your findings in the table.

Appliance	Uses battery or mains electricity?	Appliance	Uses battery or mains electricity?

EXTRA!
List the items in and around your house which run on mains electricity.
Make a separate list of those items which run on batteries.

How to be Brilliant at Electricity, Light and Sound

Beware – electric items may be dangerous!

If simple rules are followed, electrical items are usually safe. If the rules are broken, electric items may be very dangerous. Look at the pictures below. Write a few words beside each picture explaining the danger.

> **EXTRA!**
> Design a poster to help your friends and family keep safe from the dangers of electricity.

How does electricity pass through the bulb?

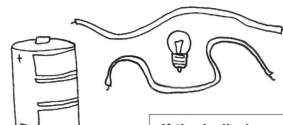

What you need:
battery (1.5 volt), bulb (1.5 – 2.5 volt),
2 pieces of wire, sticky tape, Plasticine.

Follow these instructions carefully.
❑ Attach the battery on its long side to the table using Plasticine.
❑ Use sticky tape to attach a wire to each end of the battery. Ensure that the wires make a firm connection with the middle of each end of the battery.
❑ Use Plasticine to attach the bulb on its side to the table.
❑ Using the two free ends of the wires, try to make the bulb light.

If the bulb does not light:
❑ check the connections with the battery;
❑ try touching different parts of the bulb with the wire.

Draw a picture of your circuit here:

Describe the path the electricity takes as it passes around the circuit, explaining in detail the route through the bulb.

EXTRA!
Turn the battery around. Does the bulb still light? Move the two wires to different places on the bulb. Can you get the bulb to light?

How to be Brilliant at Electricity, Light and Sound

Electricity pathways

What you need:
battery (1.5 volt) in battery holder, bulb (1.5 – 2.5 volt) in bulb holder, 3 pieces of wire (preferably with crocodile clips at each end), metal spoon. Other everyday objects made from a variety of materials: *eg paper, polythene bag, wooden spoon, mug, eraser, yoghurt pot, kitchen towel, Plasticine, paper clip, pencil with graphite showing at both ends.*

Materials that allow electricity to flow through them are called **conductors**. Materials that do not allow electricity to pass through them are called **insulators**.

Make a circuit like this:

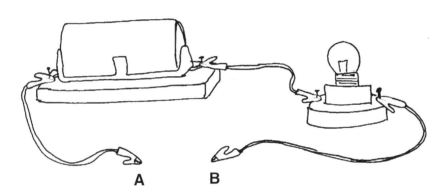

Try touching crocodile clips **A** and **B** together. The bulb should light up.

A　　**B**

Fasten crocodile clips **A** and **B** to a metal spoon.

Does the bulb still light up?

Is the electricity still flowing?

Test other everyday objects to see if they allow electricity to flow through them. Make a list of the ones that do.

EXTRA!
Which types of materials are conductors of electricity?
Which types of materials are insulators?

Make your own electric circuit quiz board

What you need:
A piece of thin card (A4 or larger), 16 two-legged paper fasteners, lots of pieces of insulated electrical wire bared at the ends (varying lengths), battery (1.5 volt), bulb (1.5 – 2.5 volt), paper (optional), sticky tape or bulldog clips (optional).

You can use this sheet to make a quiz board to test your friends' knowledge of any topic.

Write on the top of your piece of card what your quiz will be about, eg 'Countries and their capital cities'.

Down the left hand side of the card write your 8 questions. Down the right hand side, write the answers, but in a different order from the questions.

Draw a row of dots beside each question and answer. Push a two-legged paper fastener into the card, through each dot. Then turn the card over and use wires with bared ends to connect each question with the correct answer.

Turn the card over. Test that you have wired up the quiz correctly by using a simple circuit with a bulb and battery. The bulb should light up each time you touch the fasteners beside a matching question and answer with the wires from your circuit. Give your quiz and circuit to a friend and test their knowledge!

To make up a new quiz, fasten clean sheets of paper over your questions and answers and write new ones on top. Make sure to check that all the connections at the back are correct for your new quiz.

Countries and their capital cities	
Questions	Answers
France •	• Madrid
Wales •	• London
Ireland •	• Paris
Spain •	• Dublin
Scotland •	• Rome
England •	• Stockholm
Italy •	• Cardiff
Sweden •	• Edinburgh

front

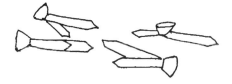

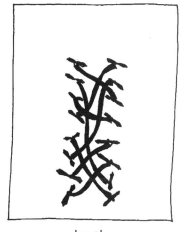

back

EXTRA!
Devise other questions and answers relating to school work you have recently carried out, football teams and the names of the grounds at which they play, foods and the countries they originate from or scientists and their inventions, etc.

Putting bulbs and buzzers in circuits

What you need:
2 batteries (1.5 volt) with or without battery holders, bulb (3.5 – 4.5 volt) in a bulb holder, buzzer (preferably 4.5 volt, but 6 volt would do), 2 or 3 connecting wires (with or without crocodile clips), screwdriver.

How easy is it to connect a bulb or a buzzer in a circuit? One of them is straightforward, but the other component needs a little bit of care – but which is which?

Make your predictions below:

I predict that the _____ **will** be more straightforward to connect.

I predict that the _____ **will not** be so straightforward to connect.

Make a circuit using the two batteries, connecting wires and the bulb in a bulb holder. Make sure that the positive terminal (+) of one battery is connected to the negative terminal (−) of the other battery. Check the connections.

Does the bulb light?

Undo the connections to the bulb holder and turn it right around and connect it again.

Does the bulb light now?

Now make up a circuit using the two batteries, connecting wires and the buzzer. Check the connections carefully.

Does the buzzer 'buzz'?

Undo the connections to the buzzer and turn it right around and connect it again.

Does the buzzer 'buzz' now?

Which component is more straightforward to connect? Why?

EXTRA!
Look at the buzzer circuit when the buzzer works and when it does not. Make up a rule to tell your friends how to connect the buzzer correctly.

Making switches

What you need:
battery (1.5 volt), bulb (1.5 – 2.5 volt) in a bulb holder, 3 wires with bared ends (with or without crocodile clips), screwdriver (if not using crocodile clips), a small piece of pinboard or stiff styrofoam, 2 drawing pins, a bought switch (optional), one or more of the following: a paper clip, a flexible steel strip or a piece of thick card wrapped in silver foil.

Make a circuit using the battery, the bulb and the two wires. Ensure that the bulb is screwed into the bulb holder and that the connections are sound.

Investigate how many different ways you can find to turn the bulb on and off. Draw a diagram of your circuit and explain all the different ways you have found.

It is possible to turn the circuit on and off in five places.

Adding a switch to your circuit will make it even easier to turn the bulb on and off.

Make one or more of the switches shown here:

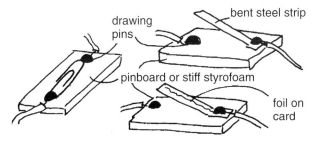

drawing pins

bent steel strip

pinboard or stiff styrofoam

foil on card

Place the switch you have built in your circuit and make the bulb go on and off. Try using another type of homemade switch and a bought switch (if available). Which one works best?

Place your switch in another place in the circuit. Does it switch the bulb off and on there as well?

EXTRA!
Replace the bulb with a buzzer. If it doesn't work, connect the buzzer the other way round.

How to be Brilliant at Electricity, Light and Sound

Morse code

What you need:
2 batteries (1.5 volt) with or without battery holders, bulb (3.5 – 4.5 volt) in bulb holder, 3 connecting wires (with or without crocodile clips), homemade or bought switch, screwdriver. You will need a buzzer (preferably 4.5 volt, but 6 volt will do) for the **EXTRA!** activity.

An American named Samuel Morse devised a code made of dots and dashes. Messages could be sent using these dots and dashes. The invention of electricity allowed the code to be used to send messages over great distances. We call this code the **Morse code**.

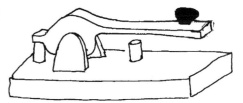

A	• –	J	• – – –	S	• • •	2	• • – – –
B	– • • •	K	– • –	T	–	3	• • • – –
C	– • – •	L	• – • •	U	• • –	4	• • • • –
D	– • •	M	– –	V	• • • –	5	• • • • •
E	•	N	– •	W	• – –	6	– • • • •
F	• • – •	O	– – –	X	– • • –	7	– – • • •
G	– – •	P	• – – •	Y	– • – –	8	– – – • •
H	• • • •	Q	– – • –	Z	– – • •	9	– – – – •
I	• •	R	• – •	1	• – – – –	10	• • • • •

Set up your circuit using both batteries and the bulb.

Now write a short message to a friend here:

Write the message in Morse Code here:

Hold the switch down a short time for a dot and long time for a dash. What will you do to show your friend each word has finished?

Your friend will need their own copy of the code, a pencil and piece of paper on which to write down the message. Send your message slowly using the switch. You will have done well if your friend can understand the message!

EXTRA!
Now try using a buzzer for your message. Devise a fair test to see whether it is easier to understand a message sent by a flashing light or by a buzzer.

Design a set of model traffic lights

What you need:
3 bulbs (1.5 – 2.5 volt) painted red, amber and green or covered in coloured see-through paper, 3 bulb holders, battery (1.5 volt), 2 pieces of soft pinboard, drawing pins, homemade or bought swtich, approximately 10 pieces of wire bared at each end, *Model traffic lights hint sheet* (page 46).

First, you need to remember the order in which the traffic lights work. Number the colours in the correct order to get the correct traffic light sequence. Start with red.

___ Green   ___ Amber   **1** Red   ___ Red and Amber   ___ Red

Use the materials listed in the **What you need** box to design your traffic lights. Use drawing pins to connect the wires to the board.

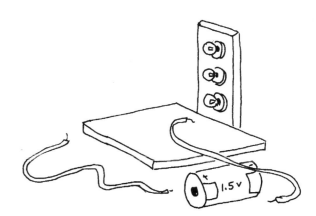

Draw your design here:

Helpful hints
If you really get stuck, your teacher has a number of hints to help you. However, make sure you have tried all your ideas before asking for the first hint!

EXTRA!
With supervision, at home or at school, time how long each coloured light stays lit on real traffic lights. Use the same times when operating your model traffic lights.

How to be Brilliant at Electricity, Light and Sound

How bright?

What you need:
3 batteries (1.5 volt) preferably in separate battery holders, 3 bulbs (4.5 volt) in bulb holders, 4 connecting wires. You will need bulbs of different voltages for the **EXTRA!** activity.

When you set up an electric circuit the bulbs are sometimes bright and sometimes dim. What factors affect how bright the bulbs are in an electric circuit? Make your prediction here:

I predict …

Investigate the effects of using different numbers of batteries and bulbs in a circuit on the brightness of the bulbs. The bulbs should be in series (in a row), as shown in the diagram.

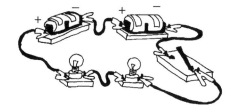

Set up the circuits as shown in the table below. Record your results for each circuit.

Number of batteries	Number of bulbs	Brightness of bulbs (dim, bright or very bright)
1	1	
2	2	
3	3	
1	2	
1	3	
2	3	
2	1	
3	1	
3	2	

Use your results to explain what affects the brightness of the bulbs.

EXTRA!
Investigate changing the size of the bulb. Does this affect the brightness of the bulb?

The lifting nail – electromagnets

What you need

3 batteries (1.5 volt) in battery holders, 2 plastic-coated wires with crocodile clips at both ends, copper wire or thin cotton-insulated wire, medium-sized iron nail, paper clips or other small metal objects. You will need iron nails or iron rods of different lengths and diameters for the **EXTRA!** activity.

Cranes in scrap yards use electromagnets to move dis-used cars around. You can make your own electromagnet by winding a wire around a nail.

Set up the equipment as shown in the diagram below. Wind the wire around the nail 10 times only. Use the whole length of the nail, as shown.

Have you ever seen cranes moving dis-used cars around in scrap yards? The crane attachment suddenly seems to stick to the cars and lift them up.

plastic-coated wire

iron nail

Safety note: The wire and nail may become very hot.

thin cotton-insulated wire (or copper wire)

How many paper clips will the nail pick up? Record your results below. Experiment with changing the number of batteries and turns of the wire. Record your results in the table.

Number of batteries	Number of turns of the wire	Number of paper clips picked up
1	10	
2	10	
3	10	
1	20	
2	20	
3	20	
1	30	
2	30	
3	30	

When you use more than one battery, check that the negative terminal of the first battery is connected to the positive terminal of the second battery.

Look closely at your results. Can you see any patterns? Write what you have found out here.

EXTRA!

Design a fair test to see if the size of the nail will affect how many items your electromagnet will pick up. Show your ideas to your teacher before you try them out.

How to be Brilliant at Electricity, Light and Sound

What you need:
2 batteries (1.5 volt) in battery holders, 2 bulbs (3.5 volt) in bulb holders, buzzer (preferably 4.5 volt), switch, 4 pieces of wire with crocodile clips attached, copy of *Cut-out circuit drawings* (page 47).

Set up circuit **A** shown below. Use the *Cut-out circuit drawings* (page 47) to copy the same circuit. Draw it in the space below. Check your drawing with someone else.

Circuit A

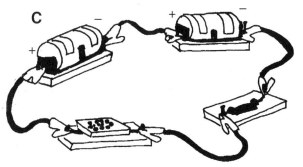

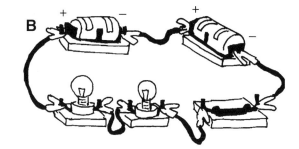

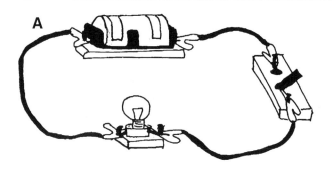

Set up circuits **B**, **C** and **D**. Make them using the *Cut-out circuit drawings*, then draw them on the back of this sheet. Check your circuits and drawings with someone else.

EXTRA!
Design a circuit of your own and make a drawing of it. Will your bulb or buzzer work?

Circuit diagrams using symbols

What you need:
2 batteries (1.5 volt) in battery holders, 2 bulbs (3.5 volt) in bulb holders, buzzer (preferably 4.5 volt), switch, 4 pieces of wire with crocodile clips attached, copy of *Cut-out circuit symbols* (page 48).

Set up circuit **A** shown below. Use the *Cut-out circuit symbols* (page 48) to make a diagram of the circuit. Check your circuit diagram with someone else. Draw your circuit diagram in the space below.

Circuit A

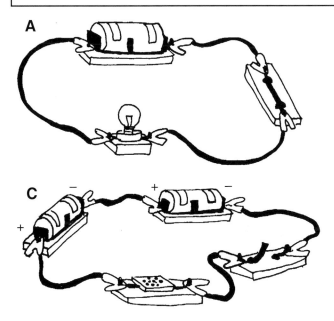

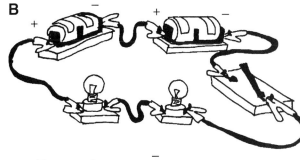

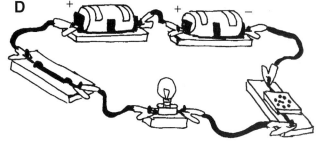

Set up circuits **B**, **C** and **D** and construct circuit diagrams using the *Cut-out circuit symbols*. Draw the circuit diagrams on the back of this sheet. Check your diagrams with someone else.

EXTRA!
Make a circuit of your own and draw a diagram of it using symbols. Will your bulb or buzzer work?

How to be Brilliant at Electricity, Light and Sound

Make a lighthouse

Make your model lighthouse using the diagram and labels below to help you.

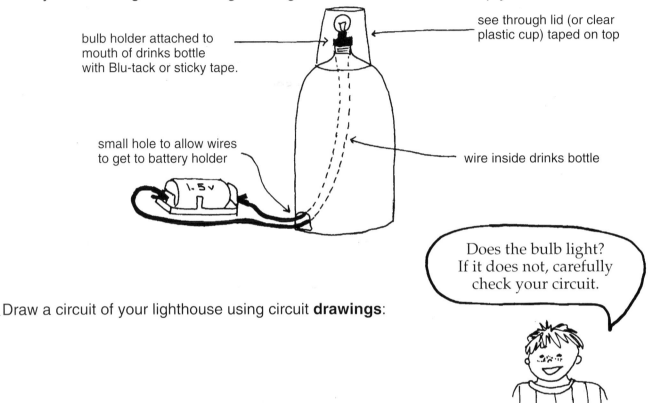

bulb holder attached to mouth of drinks bottle with Blu-tack or sticky tape.

see through lid (or clear plastic cup) taped on top

small hole to allow wires to get to battery holder

wire inside drinks bottle

Does the bulb light? If it does not, carefully check your circuit.

Draw a circuit of your lighthouse using circuit **drawings**:

Modify your model lighthouse to make the bulb flash on and off like a real lighthouse. Which component will you need to add?

Draw a circuit of your flashing lighthouse using circuit **diagrams**:

EXTRA!
Using books or CD-ROM find out what causes the light to move in a lighthouse. Why would it be difficult to get the bulb to move in your model?

Electricity detective

What you need:
2 batteries (1.5 volt) in battery holders, 3 bulbs (3.5 volt) in bulb holders, 2 switches, 4 wires (preferably with crocodile clips).

Look at each circuit diagram. Will the bulb(s) light? Will they be bright, normal or dull? Write your prediction in the space provided. Make the circuit and write what happened and why.

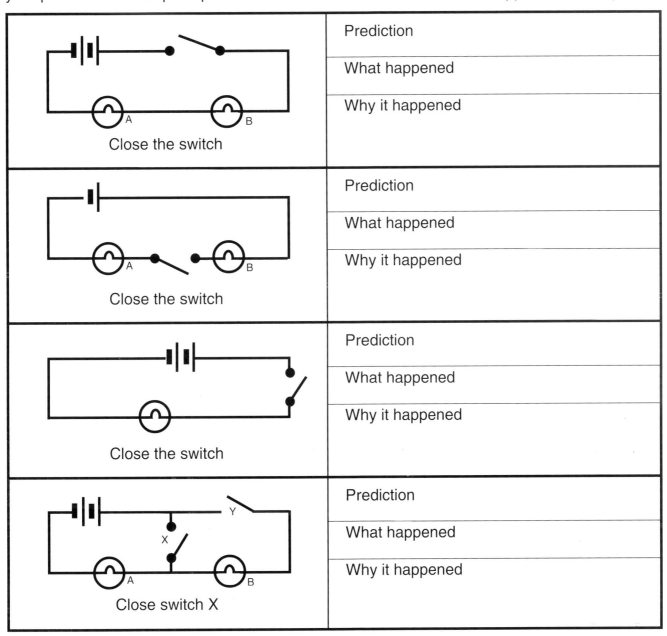

	Prediction
Close the switch	What happened
	Why it happened

	Prediction
Close the switch	What happened
	Why it happened

	Prediction
Close the switch	What happened
	Why it happened

	Prediction
Close switch X	What happened
	Why it happened

EXTRA!
Make some circuits of your own. Write a prediction, what happened and why.

How to be Brilliant at Electricity, Light and Sound

Light in our lives

Why are you unable to see anything in a darkened room?

Look at the pictures below. They show different ways that light is important in our lives. Put ticks in the boxes to show which objects are sources of light and which reflect light.

	sun	candle	torch	car wing mirror
Source of light				
Reflects light				

	table lamp	make-up mirror	light bulb	moon
Source of light				
Reflects light				

	camera with flash bulb	three-part mirror	shiny saucepans	fluorescent light bulb
Source of light				
Reflects light				

EXTRA!
Sunlight can also be a nuisance and can be harmful to us. List some ways in which we protect ourselves and our houses from the sun's rays.

What makes a shadow?

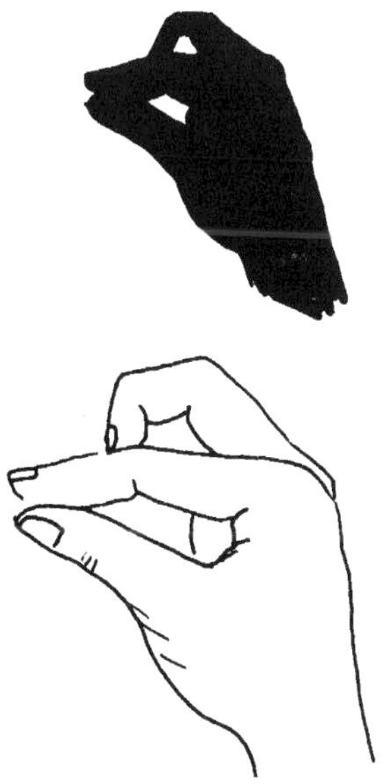

Work with a friend to sort a collection of objects made from a variety
of materials into those which you think will form a shadow and those
which will not.

One of you shines the light from the torch or projector on to a blank
wall. The other holds up each object in turn to see if it produces a
shadow on the wall. Complete the table to show your results.

Why are shadows formed? (Hint: Think about the objects which formed shadows and those
which did not. What materials are they made of?)

EXTRA!
How can you make the shadow smaller and larger?
Is the shadow always the same shape as the object making the shadow?

How to be Brilliant at Electricity, Light and Sound

When are shadows are formed?

Using a projector or torch, produce a shadow either with your hand or with an object in the classroom.

Investigate holding up different materials behind your hand or object. On which materials can you form a shadow?

Record your results in a table. The outline of the table has been drawn for you.

Cross out the incorrect answer:

Shadows are formed best on materials which

> let light through.
> do not let light through.

Shadows are formed best on materials which

> have a light colour.
> have a very dark colour.

EXTRA!
How can you make the edges of the shadow as sharp as possible?

Who's who?

What you need:
A bright source of light such as an overhead projector, a slide projector or a very bright lamp, pieces of black paper (A4 or larger), Blu-tack, white crayon or pencil, a clear wall, members of your class.

Safety note: Do not move an overhead projector while the bulb is on, or it might blow!

Follow these instructions carefully:

❑ With the help of your teacher, set up the projector near a clear wall.

❑ At head height, attach a piece of black paper to the wall using Blu-tack.

❑ Take turns standing between the light source and the sheet of paper.

❑ Adjust the position of the light so that a clear shadow of your friend appears on the paper.

❑ Carefully draw around the shadow, then put your friend's name on the back of the piece of paper.

❑ Continue until you have produced shadow pictures of all your class.

❑ Number each shadow picture: 1, 2, 3 …

❑ Display the shadow pictures around the classroom.

❑ With the help of your teacher, organize a quiz for the class. Who can recognize the most shadow pictures?

Were any of the shadow pictures hard to recognize?

Why was this the case?

Why is a shadow made when a light shines on your head?

EXTRA!
Find out what is meant by a silhouette. Did you make silhouettes of your friends?

How to be Brilliant at Electricity, Light and Sound

Reflections

What you need:
Face paint, pencil, 3 flat mirrors,
paper, sticky tape.

Sit in front of a mirror and make a
sketch of yourself in the box.

Try to make your sketch as
accurate as possible.

Do you think this is exactly as other
people see you? Put a small dab of
face paint on one side of your face
and look at your reflection again.
On which side of the drawing of
your face do you need to add the
paint mark?

Tape two mirrors together with sticky tape and stand them
upright. Put an object on the desk in front of the two mirrors.

How many images do you see?

Try moving the mirrors further apart and closer together.

Does this change the number of images you see?

Now try with the mirrors at different distances and in different
positions (for example facing each other).

Write what you have found out here:

Write your name here:

Look at the reflection of your name in the two mirrors.

Move the mirrors so that they are at such an angle to
each other that your name appears to be the right way
round.

EXTRA!
Tape three mirrors together, two
upright and one horizontal.
Look through each of the
mirrors in turn. Does your
reflection look different? Is it
always back to front?

Writing with mirrors

Can you read this?

What you need:
A large flat mirror, pens, pencils, sheets of paper.

Write your name here in capital letters.

Stand a mirror on the paper and look at the reflection of your name in the mirror.

Which letters look different?

Test other letters of the alphabet. Which look the same as their mirror image?

Write the numbers 0–9 here and try reading them through the mirror.

Write a secret message in back to front writing in the box below. Ask a friend to try to read it without using a mirror.

Join up the dots on this paper by placing a mirror upright on the page and only looking in the mirror to join them up.

EXTRA!
Design some shapes which will look exactly the same when viewed through a mirror.

Comparing images

What you need
A torch, a collection of mirrors – some flat and some curved, objects with shiny surfaces, bendable mirrors.

When you look into a mirror you see a picture of yourself reflected in the mirror. This is called an **image**.

Make a collection of different types of mirrors and investigate the different images you see.

Try to sort your mirrors into groups which produce the same sorts of images. Write down what you have found here:

Do any of your mirrors enlarge the image?

Do any of your mirrors curve inwards?

Do you have any mirrors that curve outwards?

Do any of your mirrors make things look smaller?

Investigate how the image changes when you bend a bendable mirror. Try bending the mirror so that the surface you look into is curved first outwards, then inwards.

Compare the images you see with those you see when you look into both sides of the surface of a shiny spoon or the shiny surface of a saucepan. Does it make a difference how close to your face you hold the spoon?

How do different types of mirrors help us in everyday life?
Fill in the table below.

Mirror	Type of image produced
shaving mirror	
car wing mirror	
flat mirror	
mirror curved outwards	
mirror curved inwards	

EXTRA!
Make a collection of shiny objects which can be used as mirrors. Group them according to the different types of images they produce.

Tall mirrors – do you need them?

What you need
A tall mirror, dressmaker's measuring tape or metre stick, sticky tape, paper or card, pencil, a selection of small mirrors (these could be made by sticking aluminium foil onto card).

How big does a mirror have to be so that you can see all of your body in it?

Work with some friends to investigate how the size of your mirror image compares to your actual height. Tape the dressmaker's measuring tape or metre stick to the side of the tall mirror.

Stand in front of a mirror in a position where you can see both your head and your toes. Mark the position of your feet on the ground. Use the measuring tape to measure how high your image in the mirror appears **to you**. Do this for everyone in the group. Everyone should stand the same distance from the mirror. Now measure your actual heights. Write the results in the table.

Name	Height of mirror image	Actual height

Do you notice any link between the measurements?

Try making your own model cut-out people of different sizes. Stand them in front of different sized mirrors. Investigate which are the most suitable sized mirrors for your cut-out people.

Write down what you have found out here:

EXTRA!
Try to find out how you might see many images of yourself in a mirror.

Make a periscope

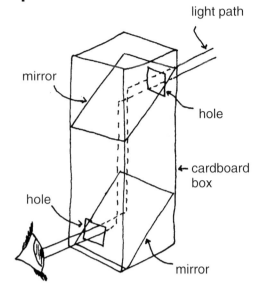

light path

mirror

hole

cardboard box

hole

mirror

What you need
A cardboard box such as a cracker box, two small square flat mirrors the same size, scissors, Blu-tack.

Wouldn't it be useful to be able to see round corners or to be able to see over the tops of people's heads?

This can be done by using an instrument called a **periscope** which is a tube with two mirrors. The top mirror reflects light downwards on to the second mirror. The second mirror reflects the light into your eyes.

You can make your own periscope using a cardboard box and two mirrors.

❑ Using scissors, make two slits – one at each end of the box.

❑ Slide a mirror into each slit so that they are facing each other at the same angle (as in the picture).

❑ Fasten them in place with Blu-tack.

❑ Cut a viewing hole in the box so that you can look into the bottom mirror and another hole at the top of the box on the side opposite to your viewing hole, to let the light rays in.

Submarines use periscopes to see what is going on above water.

Test your periscope in the classroom. Put some objects on a high shelf and try to see them using your periscope. Can you see objects on top of a table if you are crouched on the floor?

EXTRA!
Test out your periscope in the school grounds.
Does it help you to see round corners?

How to be Brilliant at Electricity, Light and Sound

Seeing the light

Complete the following sentence using the words below:

I can see light sources such as a _____ , _____

and _____ because the _____ from them enters my _____ .

Use lines with arrows to show how we can see the light sources below:

Jenny's kite is stuck in a tree. There is no light source on the kite, but she can see it because the light from the Sun reflects off the kite and then into her eyes.

Draw arrows to show the path the light takes to enable Jenny to see the kite.

EXTRA!
On the back of the page, draw a picture and add arrows to show how you can see your reflection when you look in a mirror.

How to be Brilliant at Electricity, Light and Sound

Light quiz

How many of the following questions can you answer correctly? When you have completed the quiz, swap with a friend and check each other's answers.

Draw the mirror image of the following letters and numbers.

A 3 Z D 9

Write down two situations when a periscope might be useful.

1

2

Describe the image you will see in each type of mirror. Will the image be bigger or smaller? Which way up will it be?

shaving mirror	flat mirror	car wing mirror

This picture shows the mirror image of a clock. What is the real time it is showing?

What would this coded message say if you read it through a mirror?

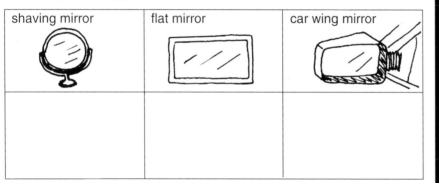

How are shadows formed?

EXTRA!
Make up your own light quiz and test it on a friend.

Different sounds

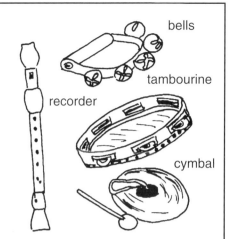

bells
tambourine
recorder
cymbal

What you need
A variety of junk materials to make musical instruments, *eg elastic bands, empty margarine tubs, milk bottles and metal cans, small cardboard boxes, drinking straws, rulers, metal spoons, wooden beads or rice for shakers, etc.*

Sounds are produced by musical instruments in a number of different ways. They can be:

 plucked    blown    banged    shaken

Look at the pictures around the page. Sort the instruments into groups depending on how the sound is produced and fill in the chart.

pan-pipes

violin

drum

These instruments are plucked.	These instruments are blown.
These instruments are banged.	**These instruments are shaken.**

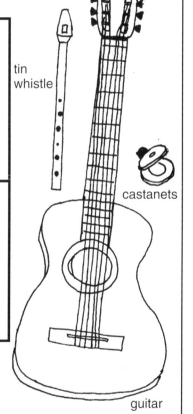

tin whistle

castanets

guitar

Now make your own musical instruments out of the junk materials provided. Try to produce sounds in different ways such as banging, plucking, scraping.

Write about your experiments here:

EXTRA!
Try making different notes with the instruments you have made. Can you play a musical scale?

How to be Brilliant at Electricity, Light and Sound

Bottle music

What you need
10 identical empty bottles, a metal spoon, a jug, water.

Tap an empty bottle gently with a metal spoon and listen to the sound it makes. Pour some water into the bottle and tap the bottle again. Does the sound change? Add a little more water and see if this makes any difference to the sound.

I found out that …

Now place your empty bottles in a line. Leave the first bottle empty and then pour increasing amounts of water into the bottles until the last bottle in the line is about three quarters full.

Tap each bottle gently with the spoon and listen to the sound it makes.

See if you can tune the bottles by adding or taking away water so that tapping each bottle makes a different note on a musical scale. You may find it easier to tune your bottles if you compare the sound of your bottle scale with one played on a piano.

Try playing some tunes on your musical instrument.

Does it make any difference to the sound if you tap the bottles above or below the water levels?

EXTRA!
See if you can make different notes by using different types of bottles.

How to be Brilliant at Electricity, Light and Sound

Bang the drum

The top of a drum is called the **drumhead**.

What you need
A range of containers *eg plastic bowls, margarine tubs, tin cans, cardboard boxes, biscuit tins*. Cling film, plastic sheeting of different thicknesses, sticky tape, elastic bands, scissors, grains of rice, dowel rods, scraps of material, wool, ping-pong balls, cotton reels, glue.

Make some drums using the containers provided. If your containers don't already have lids, you can make drumheads out of cling film, a plastic bag or some plastic sheeting. Fasten the drumheads to the drums with elastic bands or tape. The drumhead vibrates when you hit it, producing a sound.

Investigate the different sounds each drum makes. Which is the loudest? Which is the quietest?

Try putting some rice grains on the drumhead. What happens to the rice when you tap the surface of the drums?

Make some beaters for your drums using scrap materials. You could use dowel rods for the handles. Investigate making the heads of the beaters out of cotton reels, ping-pong balls or wool.

Do different beaters make different sounds?

Put your drums on different surfaces. Does the sound increase or decrease when you play them?

Write down the results of your investigations here:

EXTRA!
Investigate the effect of filling the drums with water or sand.

How to be Brilliant at Electricity, Light and Sound

Pan-pipes

What you need
Drinking straws, scissors, sticky tape.

If you blow down a pipe or tube you make the air in the pipe vibrate. The vibrations make a sound. The wind instruments in an orchestra work in this way. Oboes, clarinets and flutes are all wind instruments.

Pan-pipes are another kind of wind instrument. They are easy to make.

First, try blowing across the end of a drinking straw. What sound does it make?

Now flatten one end of the straw and cut about one or two centimetres off each side. Put the straw into your mouth and blow. Can you make a sound now?

Cut about two centimetres off the bottom end of the straw and blow again. What happens to the musical note? Is the note higher or lower?

Cut off a little more off the end of the straw and blow again. What difference can you hear?

cut   cut

Pan was a Greek god. He is supposed to have played a musical instrument made out of reeds of different lengths fastened in a row.

To make your pan-pipes, cut the straws so that they are different lengths. Line them up so that the longest straw is at one end of the row and the shortest straw is at the other end. Tape the straws together and play a tune on the pipes by blowing down the ends of them.

EXTRA!
You can make different notes on a wind instrument by making holes along the length of the pipe. Try this with your pan-pipes and see what sounds you can make.

Scrapers

What you need
Blocks of wood of different sizes, a variety of sheets of sandpaper ranging from rough to fine, empty margarine tubs, empty matchboxes, glue, scissors.

Make some simple scrapers by sticking pieces of sandpaper to blocks of wood. Use scissors to cut the sandpaper to the right size for your wood blocks.

Investigate what sounds you can make by rubbing the blocks together.

❑ Try varying the roughness of the sandpaper. Does it make any difference to the loudness of the sound produced?

❑ What happens to the sound when you change the size of the wood block?

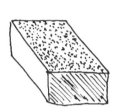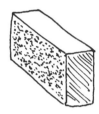

Record your results in the table below:

Size of wood block	Thickness of sandpaper	Sound produced (loud or quiet)

Investigate what happens when you replace the blocks of wood with other containers such as empty margarine tubs or matchboxes. Write here what you found out.

EXTRA!
Work with a group of friends to form a percussion band using your scrapers as musical instruments. Play different rhythms using your scrapers.

How to be Brilliant at Electricity, Light and Sound

Musical notes

The **pitch** of a sound means how high or low the sound is.

What you need
A wooden box with no lid, elastic bands of different thicknesses, bottles (all of the same size), water, tubes of different lengths but the same diameter, string, thick dowel rod, a (drum) beater, block of wood, thin wire, two wedges, different-sized weights.

Look at the pictures of home-made instruments. Write underneath each how you think you could change the pitch (make high sounds and low sounds) on the instrument.

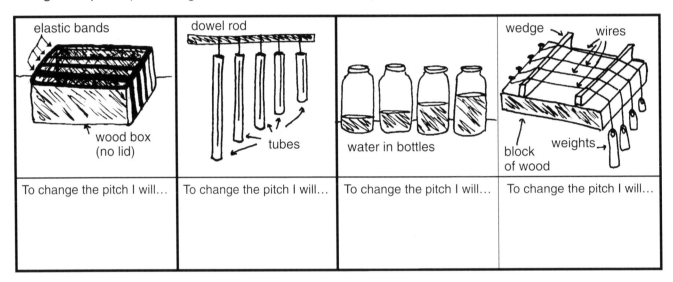

elastic bands / wood box (no lid)	dowel rod / tubes	water in bottles	wedge / wires / block of wood / weights
To change the pitch I will…	To change the pitch I will…	To change the pitch I will…	To change the pitch I will…

Now make the instruments using the things listed in the **What you need** box and investigate making notes of different pitch.

Do your investigations confirm your predictions?

Using what you have learned, write how you could change the pitch of a note for these instruments. Choose a different way each time.

guitar	**violin**

EXTRA!
List six different musical instruments and say how you can change the pitch of the notes.

How to be Brilliant at Electricity, Light and Sound

Making sounds

Sounds are made when objects vibrate.

What you need
A ruler, a felt-tip pen, paper, sticky tape.

Hold a ruler down firmly over the edge of a table. Flick the edge of the ruler so that it makes a sound. Watch the ruler vibrate.

Investigate what happens if you shorten the length of the ruler that is hanging over the edge of the table and flick the ruler again. Is the sound that is made now higher or lower? Write your results in the table.

Length of ruler over table edge	High or low sound	Fast or slow vibrations

Tape a felt-tip pen on to the end of the ruler so that the pen sticks out beyond the ruler edge. Ask a friend to hold a piece of paper so that it is touching the pen. Flick the ruler again and you should see the pen trace the shape of the vibrations on to the paper.

Try altering the length of the ruler overhanging the edge of the table. Flick the ruler each time and the pen will record the shape of the vibrations on to the paper. Cut out your vibration pictures and stick them here (or on the back of the sheet, if you need more room).

What conclusions can you make about the shape of the vibrations and the length of the ruler overhanging the edge of the table?

EXTRA!
Try the activity again using rulers of different lengths.

How to be Brilliant at Electricity, Light and Sound

Make a speaking tube

You can feel your voice box vibrating in your throat when you speak.

Hum a small tune quietly to yourself and feel the vibrations. Does it make any difference how loudly you hum?

Make a speaking tube to help you understand how your voice box works.

❑ Cut a piece of balloon large enough to fit over the end of a cardboard tube.
❑ Stretch the piece of balloon very tightly and secure it over the tube with an elastic band.
❑ Cut a slit in the piece of balloon and then blow into the other end of the tube.

What happens?

Investigate ways of making the sound higher or lower.

Write about your experiment here, including your results.

Blow up a balloon, then stretch the neck of the balloon as you release the air from it. Can you make high-pitched sounds and low-pitched sounds?

EXTRA!
Try making different sized speaking tubes using smaller and larger cardboard tubes. What difference does this make to the pitch and loudness of the sounds you produce?

High tension

I can see the strings vibrating when they are plucked.

What you need
A piece of wood, a piece of fishing line (or thin wire), a drawing pin or nail, two wedges, weights of different sizes, a stringed instrument such as a guitar.

Work with a group of friends. First, investigate how the sound is produced when a stringed instrument such as a guitar is played.

❑ How do you get high notes or low notes?
❑ What happens when you turn the keys at the neck of the instrument?
❑ What happens when you press down on the strings in different positions?

Make your own stringed instrument by stretching a piece of fishing line or wire across a piece of board. Use two wedges to hold the line up.

This diagram will help you:

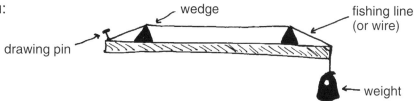

Hang a weight on the end of the line to increase the tension on the line. Now try plucking the wire between the two wedges. What sort of sound do you hear?

Try moving one of the wedges closer to the other and pluck the line again. Is the sound you make higher or lower now?

Keep moving the wedge, each time plucking the wire and listening to the sound you produce. Record your results in a table in the box below:

How do you think the length of the line affects the sound which is produced?

EXTRA!
Try changing the size of the weight on the end of the fishing line to see if you can make higher or lower notes.

How to be Brilliant at Electricity, Light and Sound

Telephone call

What you need
2 empty yoghurt pots or plastic cups, scissors or large needle for making holes, a long length of string, cotton or thin wire, piece of tubing, 2 funnels.

You will need to work with a friend for this activity.

See if you can make a telephone using some of the items listed in the **What you need** box. You could try using different mouthpieces and earpieces and different types of telephone connections such as string, wire, cotton or tubing.

This diagram will help you:

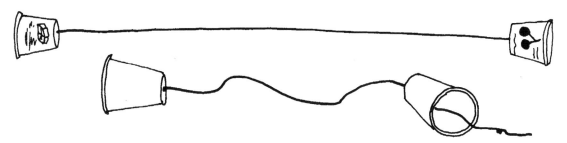

Test out your telephone to see how well it works. Make sure you carry out your test in a quiet part of a classroom or in the corridor at a quiet time. Keep the connecting string or wire as tight as possible. Talk very quietly to your friend. Can your friend hear you through the earpiece?

What happens if you and your friend move towards each other so that the connecting string is loose?

Which make more effective mouthpieces and earpieces – yoghurt pots or funnels?

What difference does it make if you use a longer connecting string?

EXTRA!
Design a telephone system linking four people together.

Sounds travel

What you need
2 pieces of string (each about a metre long), other pieces of string of the same length but different thicknesses, nylon cord, different-sized spoons and forks, other metal objects.

Carry out an investigation to find out how well sounds travel through different materials.

Tie a spoon on the ends of two pieces of string, each about a metre long. Let the spoon dangle down by holding the ends of the string. Hold the ends of the string to your ears and swing the spoon gently so that it bangs against a table or other surface.

What difference in the sound is there when you swing the spoon against the table without holding the strings to your ears?

Try using:

different-sized spoons   forks   other metal objects

Record your results in the space below, listing the different objects you used and the type of noise you heard. What difference did the size of the spoons make?

Investigate whether sound travels better if you use thicker string or nylon cord. Write in the box below what you found out:

EXTRA!
Make some cardboard earpieces to put on the ends of the string. Does this make a difference to the sounds made?

How to be Brilliant at Electricity, Light and Sound

Tick-tock

What you need
A ticking watch or clock, a wooden desk or table, a metal tube such as a pipe, a metre ruler, sheets of paper or card, cardboard tubes, sticky tape.

Carry out an investigation to find out whether sound travels through wood and metal.

Place a ticking watch or clock on the desk. Can you hear the ticking sound?

Put your ear to the desk. Can you hear the sound of the ticking now?

How far can you move away from the watch and still hear the ticking sound?

Repeat the experiment on different surfaces such as metal or plastic. Record your results in the table below:

Surface material	Distance sound travelled

Invent a listening device to make it easier for you to hear the watch ticking (use the scrap materials listed in the **What you need** box).

Draw a diagram of your listening device here:

EXTRA!
Carry out an investigation to see how far sound travels using your special listening device.

Absorbing sounds

What you need
Foam rubber, polystyrene packaging, newspaper, cotton wool, corrugated cardboard, a padded envelope, a selection of fabrics, other scrap materials, a small cassette recorder and a cassette tape or small battery operated radio, a cardboard box large enough to hold the cassette recorder or radio.

Design an experiment to find out which materials are most effective at absorbing sound. Write about your experiment in the box below.

List the equipment you have used and describe how you carried out your experiment.

How did you make sure you carried out a fair test?

What were your results and what did you find out?

EXTRA!
What other ways can you think of for us to protect ourselves from unwanted sounds?

Model traffic lights hint sheet

This sheet is for use with page 15.

Cut up the hints and place them in appropriately numbered envelopes.

Give them to the children, one at a time, when they get stuck.

HINT 1

Ensure that the battery is attached to the green bulb holder and to the switch.

HINT 2

Ensure that:
- one wire goes from the battery to the green bulb holder
- a second wire goes from the same terminal of the green bulb holder to the amber bulb holder
- a third wire goes from the same terminal of the amber bulb holder to the red bulb holder

HINT 3

The switch must be able to come into contact separately with the wire going to:
- the red bulb holder
- the red and amber bulb holders
- the green bulb holder
- the amber bulb holder

HINT 4

The switch must come into contact with the wires going to the bulb holders in the correct order, which is:
- red bulb holder
- red and amber bulb holder
- green bulb holder
- amber bulb holder

HINT 5

Cut-out circuit drawings

Cut along the dotted lines.

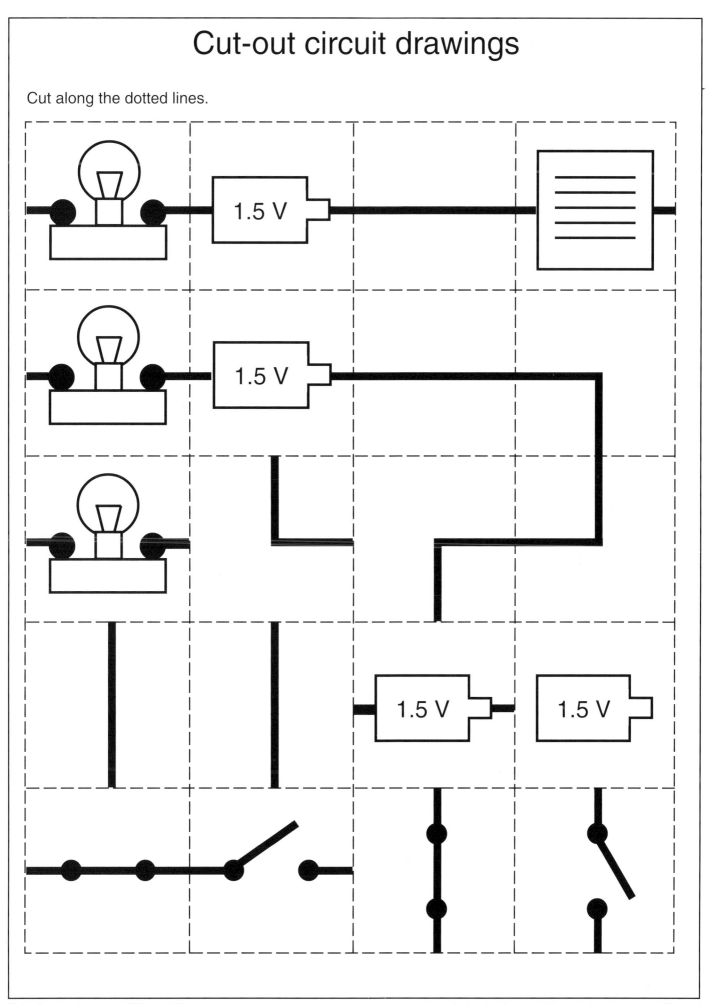

How to be Brilliant at Electricity, Light and Sound

Cut-out circuit symbols

Cut along the dotted lines.

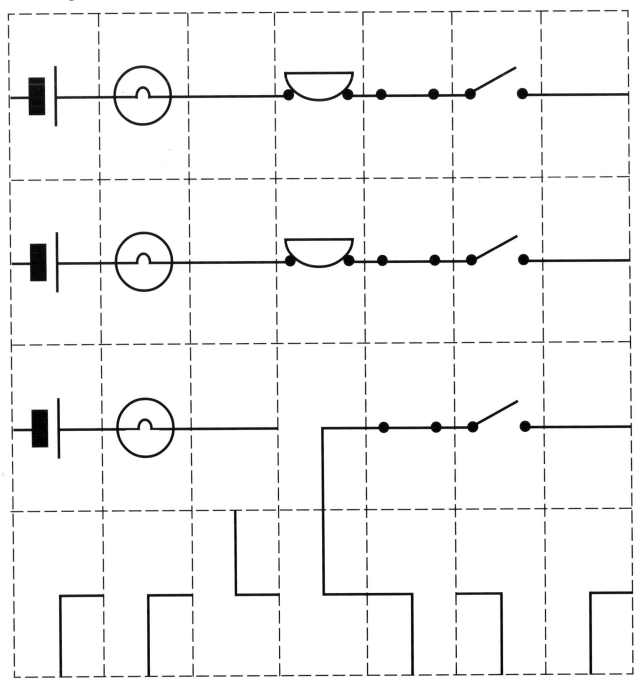